Scan the QR code
to read and listen to the
glossary words for FREE!

glossary - Meanings of words.

Every Cherry Publishing, an imprint of Sweet Cherry Publishing Limited.

Published in the UK by Sweet Cherry Publishing Limited, 2024
Unit 36, Vulcan House, Vulcan Road,
Leicester, LE5 3EF, United Kingdom

Nauschgasse 4/3/2 POB 1017
Vienna, WI 1220, Austria

2 4 6 8 10 9 7 5 3 1

ISBN: 978-1-80263-354-2

Easier Classics
Frankenstein

Original story by Mary Shelley.
Text based on the adaptation by Gemma Barder.
Illustrations by Nick Moffatt.

www.everycherry.com

Printed and bound in China

Every
Cherry

FRANKENSTEIN

MARY SHELLEY

The Creature

Victor Frankenstein

Eliza

Henry

William

Chapter 1

My name is Victor Frankenstein.

I grew up in a town called Geneva in Switzerland. I lived with my mother, father and brother, William.

*When I was eight years old, an **orphan** named Eliza came to live with us.*

We became friends straight away.

orphan - A child whose parents have died.

Eliza, William and I often played with our friend Henry in the woods, near our home.

We liked learning about **nature**. We explored where animals lived and found lots of different plants.

As I grew older, I read more and more about **nature**. I became obsessed with *how* life was created. *How* did the **spark of life** begin and what gave it power?

nature - The world of plants and animals.

spark of life - The energy inside a person that makes them alive.

One evening, there was a huge storm outside our house. I watched it from my bedroom window.

A huge **bolt of lightning** struck our chimney, and bricks fell to the ground.

This was nature at its most powerful.

bolt of lightning - The flash of light when lightning happens.

As I grew older, I wanted to learn as much as I could about nature. I applied to all the top **universities** in Europe to **study** the science of nature.

Life was perfect, until my mother became ill. No medicine could make her better. I watched as the spark of life inside her slowly faded away.

Sadly, she died.

universities - A place for grown-ups to learn, once they have finished school.

study - To learn about something.

Chapter 2

After my mother died, I wanted to learn all I could about the spark of life.

The time came for me to start studying Science at university.

I listened carefully in all of my lessons, learning as much as I could.

One night, As I was reading textbooks in the library, my **professor** came to talk to me.

'Young man,' he said. 'You are always in the library. Why don't you go out and have fun with your friends?'

'Thank you, sir, but I am not here to have fun. I am here to learn,' I replied.

professor - A teacher at university.

My professor looked at me, thinking carefully, and said, 'Follow me.'

I followed him to a dark, dusty corner of the library. He searched the shelves and handed me a heavy, old book.

'This is a strange book. You will need a big **imagination** to understand it, but I think you will enjoy it,' **explained** my professor.

imagination - Having a new idea
from thinking creatively.

explained - To help someone
understand.

I took the book back to my room.
My **student apartment** had a
bedroom and a small **laboratory**
where I did my science **experiments**.

I began reading the book.

It was filled with the strangest
experiments and ideas. It said that
scientists had created the spark of
life using lightning.

student apartment - A place where someone lives when they go to university.

laboratory - A special room with equipment to do experiments in.

experiments - Testing an idea.

I began to get excited. Lightning was a form of **electricity**. It had a lot of power. I knew it made our hair stand up and the air around us buzz.

It made sense to me that it could also create life.

Before I knew it, I had spent all night reading. Now I was ready to try the things I had read about.

electricity - A form of energy, seen in lightning and the power that makes electrical items work.

Chapter 3

Over the next few months, after my lessons, I would rush to my laboratory to do my experiments.

I studied the human body and what created life and caused death.

I was working towards my secret goal: I was going to create my own **creature** and bring it to life!

creature - A living thing, like an animal.

After weeks of working in secret,
my creature was almost ready.

It lay on my laboratory table, still
and silent. I dressed it in my clothes.
They were too small for its big body.

Now, all I needed was lightning.

Lightning would give my creature
the spark of life.

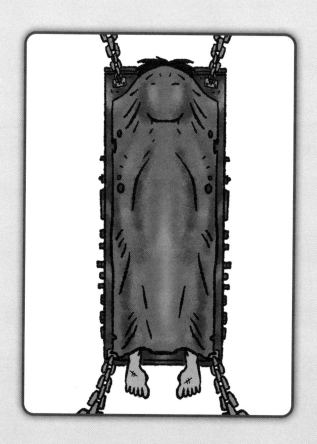

Chapter 4

After waiting for weeks and weeks, one night, a rainstorm began outside. I set up my experiment, ready to use the lightning.

I heard a loud crack, then a flash of light filled my laboratory.

Lightning flashed through my equipment, hitting my creature.

Had my experiment worked?

Suddenly, I saw something move on my table. I stepped closer.

It was breathing!

'Ngruh ...' I jumped back as the creature **groaned**.

It was alive! I had created the spark of life!

Suddenly - Quickly and not expected to happen.

groaned - Made a low noise.

The creature groaned again, moving its arms and legs. Slowly, it sat up.

'I did it!' I said to myself.

The creature finally opened its eyes and stared at me.

I saw the creature's dry yellow skin and black lips. Its long arms and legs. The dead look in its yellow eyes ... I began to feel sick.

'What have I done?' I whispered. 'I have gone against the **laws of nature**. This **hideous** creature should not be real!'

The creature stood looking at me.

It was waiting for me to tell it what to do.

laws of nature - The rules which keep plants and animals as parts of nature.

hideous - Not nice to look at.

But instead, I ran out of my apartment and into the cold, dark night. I was too scared to go home to the creature I had made.

As I was walking, a warm hand touched my shoulder. It frightened me! But it was Henry, my friend.

I hugged him. I was so **relieved** to see him. But then, I fell to the floor in **exhaustion**.

relieved - To relax because something you were worried or frightened about is not a problem anymore.

exhaustion - Feeling very tired.

Chapter 5

'Let's get you home,' said Henry.

With his arm around me, we

stumbled into my apartment.

'Your front door is open,' said Henry.

I was confused. I was sure the door

had banged shut behind me when

I had run out. I **frantically** looked

around the messy room, but nobody

was there.

The creature had run away.

stumbled - When someone trips or falls when they walk.

frantically - When someone is worried and they do something very quickly.

'I ... I do not think I feel very well. I have a fever and have not been thinking clearly,' I said.

Henry helped me to bed and told me to rest.

Henry stayed with me for months. He tidied my apartment, cooked for me and looked after me. I did not tell him about the creature. I was too **ashamed**.

ashamed - When someone feels bad about something they have done.

I often looked out of my apartment windows in case the creature came back. Each day, I **feared** I would see the terrible creature. But time passed with no **sightings** of it.

I **destroyed** my notes and equipment. All that was left was my memory of its frightening face.

feared - To be scared of something.

sightings - When someone sees something.

destroyed - To get rid of something or end it.

Chapter 6

Six months passed. I began to feel better and carried on with my studies at university, never telling anyone about the creature I had created.

Later, my friend Eliza sent me a letter. She told me that my brother, William, had gone missing.

'William!' I gasped.

Dear Victor,

Your brother, William, is missing.

We need your help to find him.

Please come home.

Your loving friend,

Eliza

I quickly ran to the train station and took the next train home to Geneva.

When I arrived home, Eliza greeted me with a hug.

She led me into the living room, where my father was, and gave us a cup of tea. He looked old and tired.

'William went to school a few days ago, but never came back home.

Someone said they saw him in the woods, but others say he was in town.

We have searched everywhere,' my father explained.

'We will find him,' I promised.

Chapter 7

The next morning, I got up early to search for William.

I walked to the forest behind the town walls. I knew the pathways, shortcuts and hiding places from playing there as a child.

I searched for him for hours. I felt sad that I had not found William. As the sun began to set, I began to walk back to town.

Suddenly, I heard a movement
behind me. I looked around.

Silence.

'William!' I called. 'Is that you?'

'It is not William,' said a low voice.
I looked through the trees but could
not see anyone. The voice scared me.

'Who is there?' I called.

Then, I saw it. Something large
and hideous.

The creature was standing in front
of me. I backed away from it.

'N-no, it c-cannot be,' I **stuttered**.
'How are you here?'

'I can explain everything,' said
the creature.

stuttered - When someone struggles to speak, so they often say the start of a word many times.

I had been so shocked to see the creature, that I didn't realise it could talk! Its voice was low and **husky**.

'Sit with me. I want to tell you my story,' it said.

I sat down and listened as the creature spoke.

husky - A rough and croaky voice.

Chapter 8

'The first time I opened my eyes, I saw you,' the creature explained.

'You looked scared. When you ran from me, I tried to follow you into the streets. But the town was confusing.

Whenever I saw another human, they would scream and run away or try to attack me.'

'So, I went into the forest, away from people and the town.

Slowly, I learnt how to **survive** in the world, to get food when I was hungry and make fire when I was cold,' said the creature.

I felt sorry for the creature. I had not thought about how it felt.
It knew nothing, and I had left it alone.

survive - To get away from danger and live.

'One day,' the creature explained.
'I saw a cottage. I hid in the shed
next to it.

I liked watching the family inside.
There was an old man, his son
and his daughter.

They did not have a lot of money or food. But they cared for each other.

They laughed and ate meals together.

I saw how kind they were. Until then, I had only seen people being mean to me.'

'One day, they were joined by a friend, but she did not speak their language. The family taught her how to speak French. I listened and learnt it too. I named the family "my cottagers".

During the cold winter, I cut firewood for them and left it outside their door.

My cottagers did not look like me. No one I had seen looked like me.'

'When the cottage was empty,
I would take books from their
shelves and teach myself to read.

I learnt about history, geography
and religion.'

Chapter 9

'I wished to enjoy the kindness this family shared,' said the creature. 'So I made a plan to **introduce** myself.

The father of the family could not see very well. I thought if he could not see what I looked like, he would not run away from me.

So, I waited until he was alone and knocked on the door.'

introduce - When someone tells someone else their name and who they are.

'He answered and did not look scared of me. I was happy. I told him I was lost, and he invited me in for tea.

I enjoyed spending time with him.

When his family came back, they screamed at me, and I ran away.

This made me feel sad and angry. I would never be friends with my cottagers. They were too scared of me.'

'You gave me these clothes when you made me,' the creature said, looking down at the **ragged** clothes.

'There was a letter in the pocket. The address was your family home in Geneva,' said the creature.

I felt anxious about what the monster was going to tell me next.

ragged - Something that is old and torn.

'Why would you come here?' I asked the creature.

'I knew that you made me but you didn't want me. So, I thought maybe your family would want me instead.

On my way to meet them, I saw a young boy who looked like you,' said the creature.

'William!' I gasped. 'What did you do to him?'

The creature looked at me with its cold, dead eyes.

'As I got closer, I realised the boy was not you. When he saw me, he was **terrified**,' said the creature.

'What happened to William?'
I shouted. The creature stared at me.

terrified - *Very scared.*

'I tried to tell him you made me. He did not listen!' it said.

'He made me angry! If I could not be part of your family, then why should he?' shouted the creature.

'You killed him!' I realised.

The creature nodded.

I fell to my knees and cried.

'Leave me alone! Leave this town and never come back!' I shouted.

But the creature did not move.

'I will only leave if you do something for me,' it said. 'I am alone because no one will love me. You made me, so make another monster like me.'

'I will not do that!' I said angrily.

'You will!' shouted the creature.
'If you do not, I will follow you
everywhere.

But, make one creature for me and
I will leave you, and all humans
alone, forever.'

I felt so confused. What would my family think of me if they met this creature? And now it was asking me to create another.

'All right. I will make you another creature as long as you agree to **disappear** forever,' I said.

'I agree,' replied the creature.

disappear - Go away.

Chapter 10

I ran home and packed my bags.

'You cannot be leaving already,'
my father said.

'Please tell Eliza that I had to leave,'
I said quietly.

I closed my suitcase and made my
way to the front door.

'Why are you leaving in such a hurry? What about William?' my father asked.

I could not tell him what had really happened to William. I felt sad and afraid.

I nearly cried as I lied, 'I have to go back to work. I will be back home soon.'

I travelled back to university, but I could not risk making another creature there.

I knew there was a laboratory in Scotland. It was on a **remote** island, so I could be alone.

As I was getting ready to leave, Henry asked to come with me. He said, 'I think you need a friend.'

I did not want him to find out about the creature. But he was **persuasive**.

'Alright,' I said. 'You can come.'

remote - A place far away from people and cities.

persuasive - Encouraging someone to do or believe something.

Chapter 11

We stayed in a small cottage on the Orkney Islands, in the north of Scotland.

Henry loved to walk and draw the beautiful scenery around us.

I had to stay alone in the laboratory, working as hard as I could.

Every night, I ate dinner with Henry.

'I know you and Eliza love one another,' said Henry. 'When will you ask her to marry you?'

I realised I cared about Eliza very much. I wanted to stop making this monster. I wanted to leave and marry Eliza.

The next evening, I unlocked my laboratory and stared at the second creature I had made.

It had the same yellow skin and scary face as the first creature.

There was a storm coming.

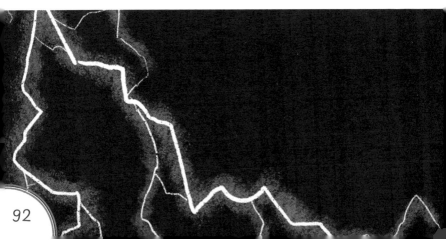

I set up my equipment, ready to bring this creature to life.

A shadow passed by the window. Just as a bolt of lightning lit up the sky, I saw the creature outside, watching.

It had come to meet its new friend.

Chapter 12

When I saw the scary creature,
I realised what I was doing was
wrong. I could not create
another monster!

I quickly stopped working.
Crash! Something had
broken the door.

The creature rushed
through the door
in anger.

'What are you doing?' it shouted.

'You promised me!'

'I cannot create another monster!'
I shouted.

The creature looked very angry.

'If you do not do this, I will always
follow you,' it said slowly. 'When you
wake up, when you sleep and when
you marry.'

Then, the monster ran into
the night.

I **wrapped** up the second creature in a sheet and dragged it to the beach.

In the middle of the dark storm, I **rowed** out to sea in a boat.

I pushed the creature over the side, into the water.

wrapped - To cover something in cloth or paper.

rowed - To move a boat with wooden sticks called oars.

I stumbled back to the cottage and got into my bed.

The next morning, I was woken up by a loud banging on the front door.

I climbed out of bed and answered the door sleepily.

There was a policeman stood in the doorway.

'Do you know a Mr Henry Clerval?' he asked.

'Yes, I do. He is my friend,' I answered.

The policeman looked at me **nervously**.

'He is missing,' he explained sadly.

nervously - The way someone does something when they feel scared or worried.

Chapter 13

'Henry!' I shouted. I rushed through the cottage, searching every room. He was nowhere to be seen and his bed had not been slept in.

'Sir,' the police officer said. 'You were seen rowing out to sea last night with a large **bundle**.'

I realised the policeman thought that I had killed Henry!

bundle - Something that is wrapped up.

The policeman grabbed my arm and asked me to come to the police station with him.

I felt dizzy and confused.

'Please ... look for Henry ... the creature,' I whispered.

I fell to the floor.

Chapter 14

I woke up in bed in the cottage.

'How are you feeling?' I turned to see my father sitting next to my bed. I was confused. What was my father doing here?

'The police told me you were very ill, so I came at once,' explained my father. 'You have been asleep for days.'

I slowly remembered what had happened to my friend.

'Henry!' I cried. 'Where is he?'

'He was murdered,' my father said sadly. I began to cry.

'The police know you did not kill him,' my father explained. 'Whoever killed him had very large hands.'

First William, now Henry. The creature was slowly killing the people I loved.

I didn't create a friend for it, so it took a friend from me.

My father and I argued. He wanted us to travel home to Geneva, but I wanted to stay and kill the creature.

After all the mistakes I had made, I decided to listen to my father.

A few days later, we set sail to go home. I could not rest for the **journey**. I kept looking for the creature, wondering if it was following me.

It was very clever, and it was angry with me. I had no idea what it planned to do next.

I promised myself that I would not let it take another person that I loved.

journey - When someone travels
from one place to another.

When we got home, I began to spend a lot of time with Eliza and my family.

Instead of learning more about Science, I became a teacher.

My memories of the creature began to fade. But still, each night, I looked for it in the garden.

A year later, I hadn't seen the monster and my worries had gone.

Chapter 15

I finally asked Eliza to marry me. She said yes.

On a sunny day, Eliza and I got married. Our family and friends celebrated with us.

While our guests were enjoying our wedding party, Eliza and I left for our **honeymoon**.

honeymoon - A holiday two people take after they get married.

We were staying in a house by a lake. It was beautiful but cold.

I went to collect wood for our **fireplace**. Suddenly, I heard a scream.

I was very scared. I remembered the last thing the creature said to me:

'I will always be with you ... even when you marry.'

fireplace - *The place in a house where you put a fire.*

I ran back to the house. I was shaking, afraid that the monster had come back.

Eliza screamed again as I rushed through the doors of the house. I felt huge relief when I saw Eliza sitting on the bed.

She was crying.

'What is wrong?' I asked.

Eliza **sobbed**, 'A monster!'

I put my arms around her and
hugged her.

Eliza never said a word again.
The creature made her feel so afraid
that she could not talk anymore.
She had changed forever.

sobbed - When someone cries very loudly.

I no longer felt afraid of the creature. I was angry. It had hurt all the people I loved. It was never going to stop. I had to get rid of the creature forever.

While my father cared for Eliza, I searched for the monster.

I knew it liked to hide in the woods, so I looked in the **woodmen's cottages** and on farms.

woodmen's cottages - A place where people who work in the woods live.

After a while, I saw large footprints, bits of food and campfires.

I **tracked** the monster to the seashore. I thought it had gotten onto a ship.

I hired a small boat and sailed to find it.

tracked - Followed using clues, such as footprints and burnt-out campfires.

Soon, the sky became darker and it grew colder. Ice began to form on the top of the water. I grew weaker and colder.

I finally found a ship and was helped on board by Captain Walton.

Until then, I had been too scared to share my story. I thought that people would hate me if they knew about my experiments.

But I needed to tell the truth.

If I cannot kill the monster, if this is the end of my story, please share it with others.

My story is a warning. We should never try to create the spark of life.

Things can go very wrong, if we try to **play God**.

play God - To do things that have a big effect on other people's lives, such as creating a monster or killing someone.

Captain Walton's Story

It was a freezing cold night when I pulled Victor Frankenstein out of his small fishing boat and onto my ship.

He was suffering from **hypothermia**. The ship's doctor put him to bed.

I visited him later that night, and he told me his strange story.

hypothermia - When someone gets very, very cold and it makes them very ill.

The following evening, the ship's doctor told me that Victor was dying.

When I went to his room, I saw a huge body crying next to his bed.

I knew at once that it was the creature Victor had spoken about.

It had the same yellow skin and eyes he had told me about.

'He was my creator,' it said to me. 'I only ever wanted him to love me.'

I slammed the door and ran away.

I called all of my **crew**, and we went back to the room. But when we returned, it was gone.

I believe the creature is still out there, living a lonely life.

crew - A group of people who work on and sail a ship.

I feel sorry for both Victor and his creature. But I cannot tell who the real monster is.

Is it the creator or the creature?

I can only tell their story.

Now you can tell it too, and learn from it what you choose to.

The End.

Mary Shelley

In 1797, Mary Shelley was born in London. She began writing *Frankenstein* when she was 18 years old.

She wrote *Frankenstein* for a competition with her husband, Percy. The competition was to see who could write the scariest story.

Mary Shelley won at a time when women were not accepted as writers.